OP 3.00

FEIFFER'S MARRIAGE MANUAL

by

Jules Feiffer

Random House New York

BOOKS BY JULES FEIFFER

Sick, Sick, Sick
Passionella
The Explainers
Boy, Girl. Boy, Girl.
Hold Me!
Feiffer's Album
Harry, the Rat with Women
The Unexpurgated Memoirs of Bernard Mergendeiler
The Great Comic Book Heroes
Feiffer on Civil Rights
Feiffer's Marriage Manual

First Printing
©Copyright, 1962, 1967, by Jules Feiffer
All rights reserved under International and Pan-American Copyright Conventions.
Published in New York by Random House, Inc., and simultaneously in Toronto, Canada, by Random House of Canada Limited.
Library of Congress Catalog Number: 67-16031
Manufactured in the United States of America

"The Tryst" originally appeared in *Playboy* Magazine.

WILL YOU MARRY ME?
WHY DO YOU ASK ME TO MARRY YOU?

BECAUSE YOU'VE GOT A ROSE IN YOUR TEETH. I'M A FOOL FOR A WOMAN WHO CARRIES A ROSE IN HER TEETH.
BUT WHAT IF I **HURT** YOU?

OH, **WOULD** YOU? NOT TOO MUCH OF COURSE. BUT TO BE HURT JUST A **LITTLE** BY A WOMAN WITH A ROSE IN HER TEETH- **WOW!**
WHAT IF I WERE UNFAITHFUL?

HOT DIGGETY! TO HAVE A WO-MAN WITH A ROSE IN HER TEETH UN-FAITHFUL TO ME! I-I SOMEHOW NEVER THOUGHT I'D RISE THAT FAR.
WHAT IF I CONSUMED YOU WITH MY STRANGE AND INSATIABLE APPETITES?

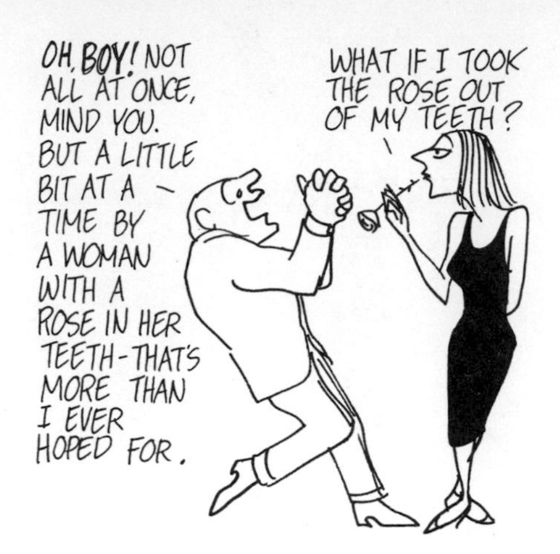
OH, BOY! NOT ALL AT ONCE, MIND YOU. BUT A LITTLE BIT AT A TIME BY A WOMAN WITH A ROSE IN HER TEETH - THAT'S MORE THAN I EVER HOPED FOR.
WHAT IF I TOOK THE ROSE OUT OF MY TEETH?

GLADYS!

I'LL PUT IT BACK, GEORGE - LOOK, GEORGE! I PUT IT BACK!

WILL YOU BE MY BEST FRIEND?
YES.

WHO I WILL MEET IN CHILDHOOD AND YOU WILL BE 3 MONTHS OLDER THAN ME AND TEACH ME TO BE FRIENDS WITH ALL THE KIDS IN THE NEIGHBORHOOD.
YES.

AND I WILL GO TO THE SAME SCHOOL AS YOU AND YOU WILL BE A LITTLE BIT BUT NOT TOO MUCH BRIGHTER THAN ME AND HELP ME WITH MY HOME-WORK.
YES.

AND I WILL GO TO THE SAME COLLEGE AS YOU AND WE WILL TRY ON EACH OTHER'S CLOTHES AND MAKEUP AND STAY UP ALL NIGHT GOSSIPING ABOUT BOYS.
YES.

AND WE WILL SHARE AN APARTMENT IN THE CITY AND DATE TOGETHER AND STAY UP ALL NIGHT DISCUSSING OUR DATES, CAREERS, POETRY, AND MUSIC.
YES.
AND WE WILL DISCOVER THAT WE HAVE DIFFERENT TASTES.
YES.
AND NO LONGER REALLY LIKE EACH OTHER.
YES.
AND BE HAPPY TO GET MARRIED AND NOT HAVE TO SEE THAT MUCH OF EACH OTHER ANYMORE.
YES.
AND BE DISAPPOINTED BY OUR HUSBANDS.
YES.
BECAUSE THEY'RE NOT LIKE OUR BEST FRIEND.

I LIE IN BED ALL DAY
HAVING FANTASIES.

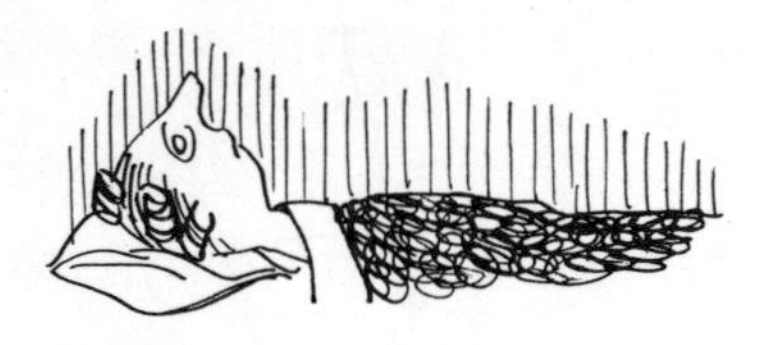

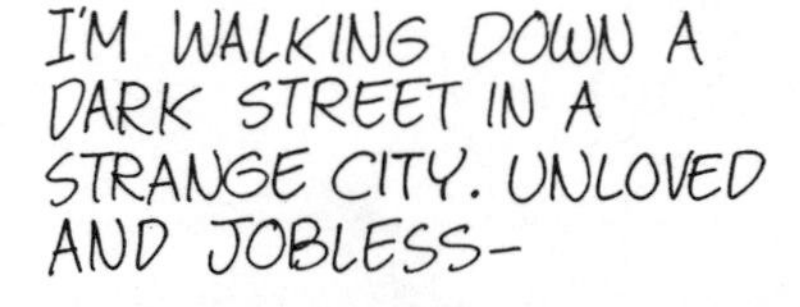

I'M WALKING DOWN A
DARK STREET IN A
STRANGE CITY. UNLOVED
AND JOBLESS-

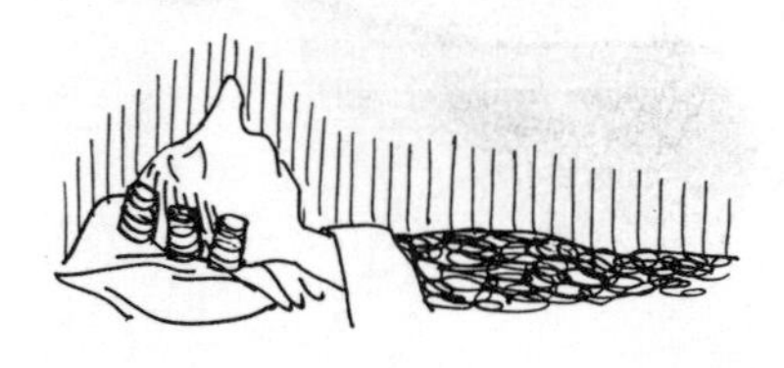

WHEN A BIG BLACK LIM-
OUSINE CAREENS AROUND
A CORNER AND KNOCKS
ME DOWN.

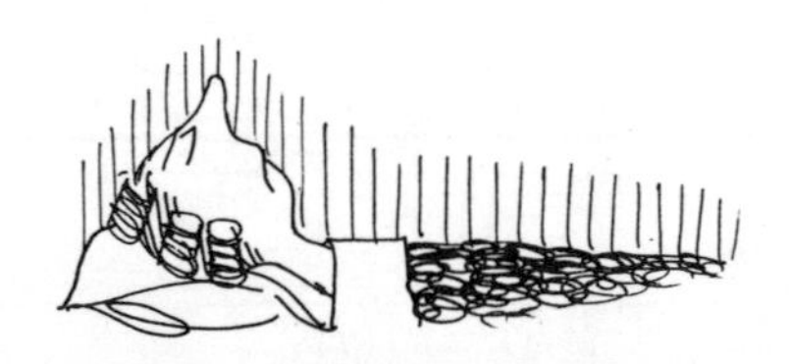

I LIE IN THE GUTTER STILL
CONSCIOUS. PEOPLE WALK
BY AND STEP ON MY HANDS.
IT BEGINS TO SNOW.

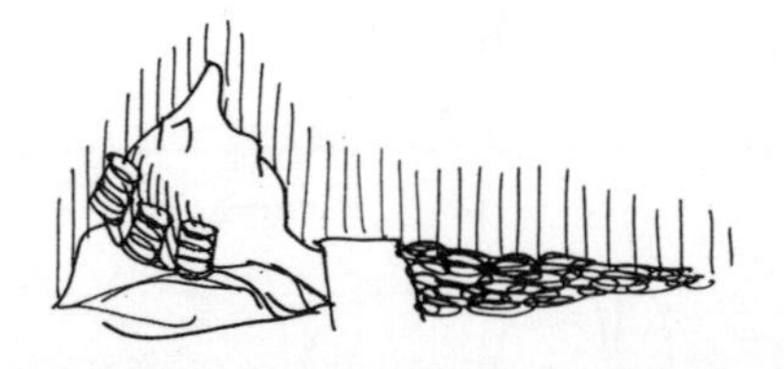

I LIE THERE FOR HOURS WHEN LAURENCE OLIVIER (THE WAY HE LOOKED TWENTY YEARS AGO) COMES ALONG. HE'S WEARING BLACK BOOTS AND CARRIES A WHIP. HE STEPS ON MY HANDS.

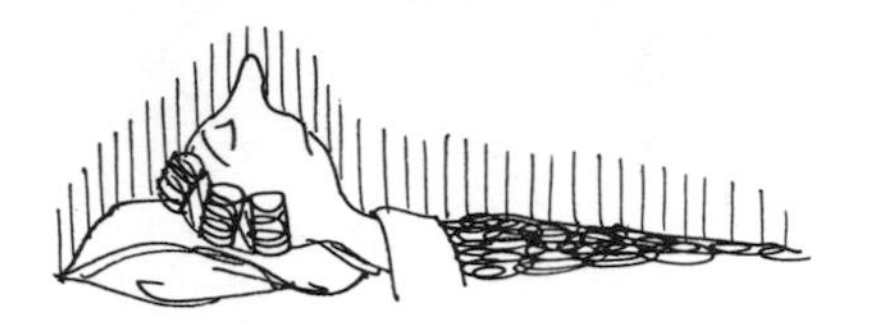

I BEGIN TO CRY. WALTER, MY HUSBAND, COMES ALONG. HE PICKS ME UP AND CARRIES ME TO A CASTLE AND BINDS MY WOUNDS AND SINGS ME SONGS AND GIVES ME PRESENTS AND SEES THAT I NEVER GO WITHOUT, EVER EVER AGAIN.

AND I LIVE HAPPILY EVER AFTER.

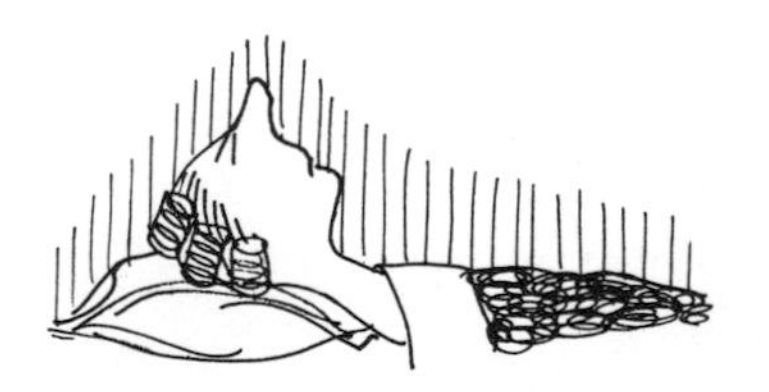

WALTER NEVER HAS UNDERSTOOD ME.

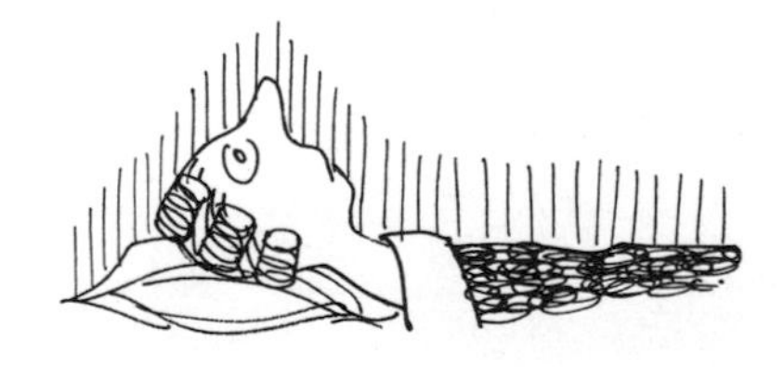

UH.
UM.
A FUNNY THING HAPPENED-
A FUNNY THING HAPPENED-
HA HA-
WE BOTH
SPOKE
AT THE
SAME
TIME.
HA HA,
YOU
GO
FIRST.
NO. NO.
YOU GO
FIRST.
NO, YOU
GO FIRST.

WELL, LET'S SEE- WELL- I DON'T REMEMBER WHAT I WAS GO-ING TO SAY.
I WENT SHOPPING TODAY. I BOUGHT BUTTER.
I NEED MORE SOCKS. I'M RUN-NING LOW ON SOCKS.
THE PHONE RANG FOUR TIMES THIS MORNING WHILE I WAS VACUUMING. THEY HUNG UP BEFORE I COULD ANSWER.
UM.
UM.
CHECK SIR.
THAT WAS LOVELY GEORGE.
WE REALLY HAVE TO GET AWAY FROM THE KIDS MORE OFTEN.

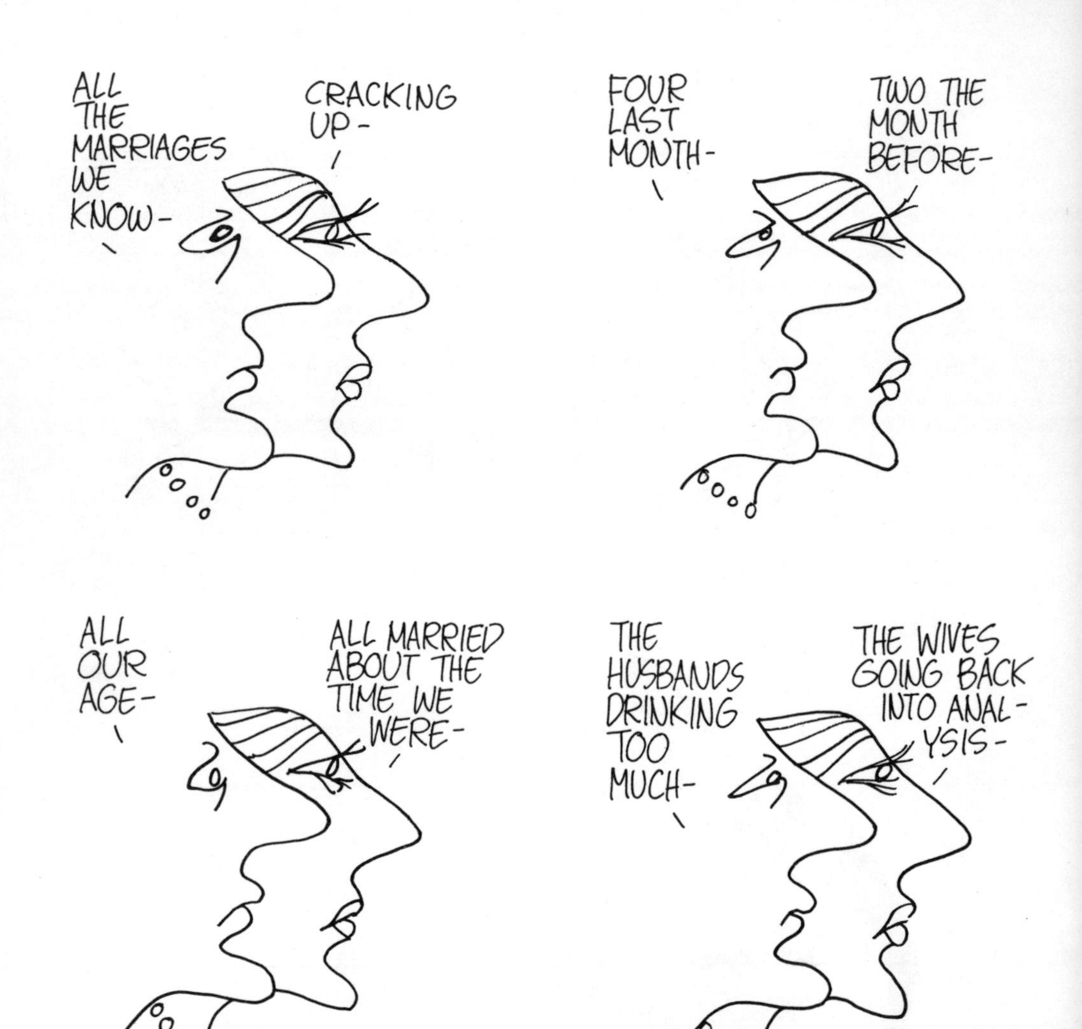
ALL THE MARRIAGES WE KNOW-
CRACKING UP-
FOUR LAST MONTH-
TWO THE MONTH BEFORE-
ALL OUR AGE-
ALL MARRIED ABOUT THE TIME WE WERE-
THE HUSBANDS DRINKING TOO MUCH-
THE WIVES GOING BACK INTO ANAL-YSIS-

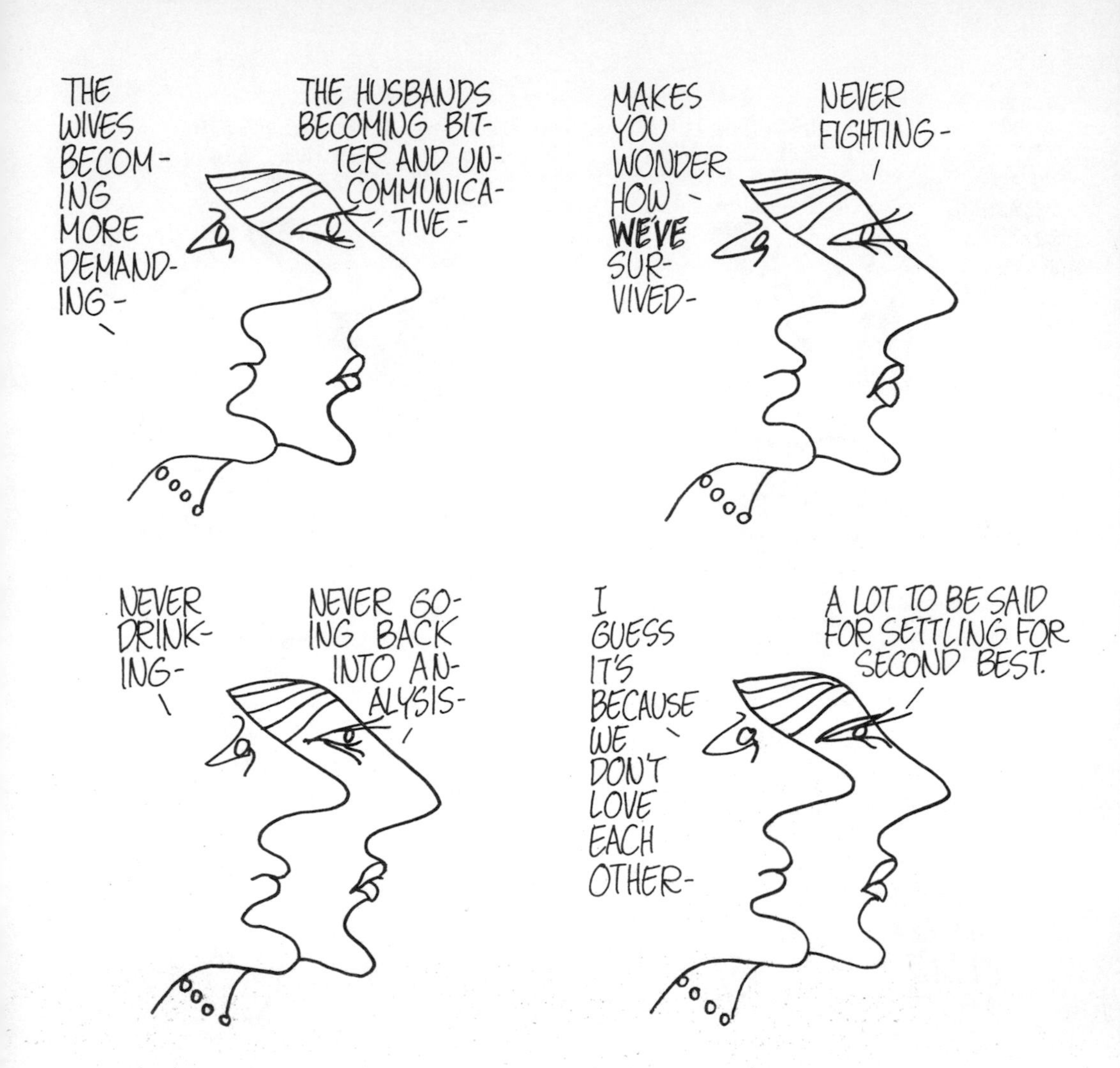
THE WIVES BECOMING MORE DEMANDING-
THE HUSBANDS BECOMING BITTER AND UNCOMMUNICATIVE-
MAKES YOU WONDER HOW **WE'VE** SURVIVED-
NEVER FIGHTING-
NEVER DRINKING-
NEVER GOING BACK INTO ANALYSIS-
I GUESS IT'S BECAUSE WE DON'T LOVE EACH OTHER-
A LOT TO BE SAID FOR SETTLING FOR SECOND BEST.

DO YOU THINK IT'S MORALLY RESPONSIBLE TO BRING A CHILD INTO THIS WORLD?
ABSOLUTELY NOT. LEON AND I HAVE GIVEN IT A LOT OF DISCUSSION.

WALTER SAYS NO TOO. HE SAYS WE HAVE NO RIGHT.
LEON SAYS THE SAME THING. "WHAT KIND OF HERITAGE ARE WE LETTING THEM IN FOR?" HE ASKS ME.

BUT I SAID TO WALTER, "WALTER, WE HAVE TO GO ON **LIVING**."
I DON'T KNOW. WE GET MORE **CONVENIENCES**, BUT DOES ANYTHING REALLY EVER GET ANY BETTER?

THAT'S WHAT WALTER SAYS. BUT I SAID, "WALTER, YOU CAN'T TURN YOUR BACK ON THE WORLD."
LEON'S MOTHER SAID EXACTLY THE SAME THING.

WELL, THE MOMENT I EXPLAINED TO WALTER THAT THE JOY OF LIVING IS TO CONQUER YOUR FEAR OF THE **UNKNOWN**, HE SAW THE LIGHT. SO TO HELP CONQUER IT WE'RE HAVING A BABY.

LEON AND I COMPLETELY DISAGREE WITH YOU. ONE NIGHT FIVE MONTHS AGO WE SPENT A WHOLE NIGHT TALKING IT OUT. WE DEFINITELY DECIDED AGAINST IT.

BEFORE - BEFORE ANYTHING HAPPENS BETWEEN US - I'VE GOT TO TELL YOU SOMETHING AND HOPE THAT IT WON'T MAKE A DIFFER-ENCE.
OH, IT CAN'T BE ALL **THAT** SERIOUS-

I'M MARRIED.
I'M GLAD YOU TOLD ME.

WELL- WHAT DO YOU THINK?
ABOUT WHAT?

ABOUT **US!** DOES IT MAKE A DIFFERENCE TO YOU? THE FACT THAT I'M **MARRIED** THAT IS?
OF COURSE NOT, WHY SHOULD IT?

WHY **SHOULD** IT? WHY **SHOULDN'T** IT? YOU MAY HAVE THE **WRONG IDEA** ABOUT ME - I DON'T PLAY AROUND A HELL OF A LOT!
HONEY, **HONEST**, IT DOESN'T MATTER IN THE **LEAST** TO ME.

OH, IT **DOESN'T** DOES IT. **WELL** MAYBE **THIS** WILL. I **LOVE** MY WIFE VERY MUCH!
MARVELOUS! ARE THERE ANY **KIDS**?

I DON'T KNOW WHAT YOU'RE TRYING TO PULL BUT AS LONG AS I'VE GONE THIS FAR YOU MAY AS WELL KNOW THE COMPLETE TRUTH- TO ME YOU'RE A ONE NIGHT ADVEN-TURE!
AND THAT'S WHAT YOU ARE TO ME, HONEY! AFTER ALL I'M MARRIED TOO.
YOU- MARRIED?
SURE-
I- I DIDN'T KNOW-
WANT TO SEE MY KIDS?
NO-NO! FOR GODSAKES- PLEASE DON'T!
LOOK, SUGAR- YOU WANT TO FORGET THE WHOLE THING?
YOU WON'T THINK I'M UNMANLY?
HONEY, TO ME YOU'RE A TIGER.
WHAT A TRULY WONDERFUL PERSON.
IF I WEREN'T HAPPILY MARRIED THAT LITTLE GIRL'S HUSBAND WOULD HAVE TO LOOK OUT.

BY THE TIME GEORGE TOLD ME HE WAS LEAVING ON A BUSINESS TRIP FOR A MONTH I HAD LOST ALL **FEELING** FOR HIM.

EACH DINNER WHEN HE'D COME HOME ID TRY TO REKINDLE THE FLAME, BUT ALL I COULD THINK OF AS HE GOBBLED UP MY CHICKEN WAS: "ALL I AM IS A **SERVANT** TO YOU, GEORGE."

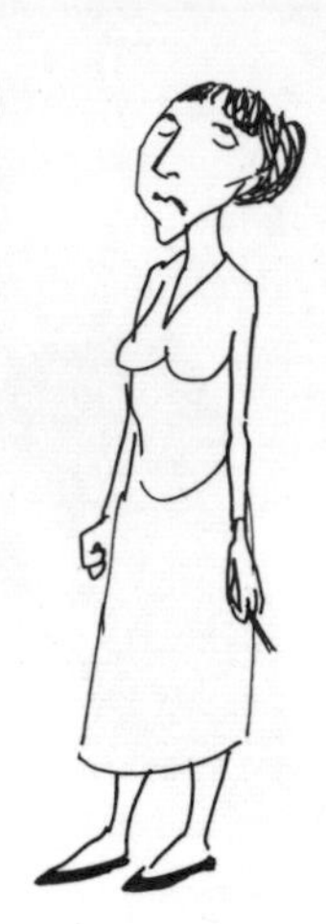

SO WHEN HE ANNOUNCED HE HAD TO GO AWAY I WAS **DELIGHTED.** WHILE GEORGE WAS AWAY I COULD **FIND** MY-SELF AGAIN! I COULD MAKE **PLANS**!

THE FIRST WEEK GEORGE WAS AWAY I WENT OUT SEVEN TIMES. THE TELEPHONE NEVER STOPPED RINGING. I HAD A **MAR**VELOUS TIME!

THE SECOND WEEK GEORGE WAS AWAY I GOT **TIRED** OF THE SAME OLD FACES, SAME OLD LINES. I REMEMBERED WHAT DROVE ME TO MARRY GEORGE IN THE FIRST PLACE.

THE THIRD WEEK GEORGE WAS AWAY I FELT CLOSER TO HIM THAN I HAD IN **YEARS.** I STAYED HOME, READ JANE AUSTEN AND SLEPT ON GEORGE'S SIDE OF THE BED.

THE FOURTH WEEK GEORGE WAS AWAY, I FELL MADLY IN LOVE WITH HIM. I HATED MYSELF FOR MY WITHDRAWAL, FOR MY FAILURE OF HIM.

THE FIFTH WEEK GEORGE CAME HOME. THE MINUTE HE WALKED IN AND SAID, "I'M BACK, DARLING!" I WITHDREW.

I CAN HARDLY WAIT FOR HIS NEXT BUSI-NESS TRIP SO I CAN LOVE GEORGE AGAIN.

IT'S TIME, AMERICA, FOR "WHAT DO YOU WANT TO BE WHEN YOU GROW UP?" THE FUN SHOW THAT ANSWERS THAT BOTHERSOME QUESTION-"WHERE DID I GO WRONG?" WHO'S OUR FIRST GUEST, FRANK?
HI, STEPPING BEFORE OUR NATION WIDE SELF HELP CAMERAS IS MRS. E.S.P. OF PATCHOGUE, L.I.

AND WHAT IS IT YOU WANTED TO BE WHEN YOU GREW UP, MRS. E.S.P.?
I COULD NEVER MAKE UP MY MIND. I USED TO WANT TO BE AN OPERA SINGER.

AN OPERA SINGER OF SONGS! HOW DOES THAT RATE ON THE AMBITION METER, AUDIENCE?
BUT I COULDN'T SEEM TO GET STARTED. THEN I WANTED TO BE A NOVELIST.
RAH

A NOVELIST OF BOOKS! HOW DOES THAT SCORE, AUDIENCE?
BUT I COULDN'T SEEM TO GET STARTED. IN THE MEANTIME I HAD GROWN UP TO BE THE ONE THING I NEVER WANTED TO BE- A MOTHER.
RAH

A MOTHER OF CHILDREN! SCORE THAT ONE, AUDIENCE!
'H RAH RAH RAH RAH RAH RAH
BUT THAT'S WHERE I WENT WRONG! IT'S HARD WORK. IT'S TOO MUCH RESPONS-IBILITY!

HA! HA! WE'RE ALL SURE YOU'RE A WON-DER-FUL PARENT, MRS. E.S.P.
IT GIVES ME NO TIME FOR MYSELF. I DON'T KNOW WHO I AM ANYMORE!

WON-DER-FUL! BUT IN YOUR HEART OF HEARTS ISN'T A MOTHER WHAT ALL YOU DEAR LADIES WANT TO BE? 'FESS UP, MRS. E.S.P. NOW 'FESS UP!
BUT NOW I KNOW WHAT I WANT TO BE! A TAP DANCER IN THE MOVIES WITH FRED ASTAIRE! NOT DANCING IN THE MOVIES WITH FRED ASTAIRE IS WHERE I WENT WRONG. YOU SAID YOU'D HELP ME. YOU SAID—

HA! HA! AMERICA KNOWS YOU'RE PULLING ITS LEG, MRS. E.S.P. AND AS A BONUS FOR COMING ON OUR SHOW WE'RE GIVING YOU ANOTHER CHILD! ISN'T THAT WON-DER-FUL, AUDIENCE?
RAHHHHHHHHHHHH
THIS WAY, LADY.

SOMETIMES WHEN I USED TO STROKE YOU TENDERLY- STROKE, STROKE, STROKE-

I USED TO THINK WHAT IF I SLOWLY INCREASED THE INTENSITY OF MY STROKE- SO THAT IT WOULD GO: STROKE, **STROKE**, **STROKE**, **POW!**

NATURALLY I WAS HORRIFIED BY SUCH THOUGHTS. HOW COULD THEY BE DIRECTED TOWARD THE WOMAN I LOVED! AND THAT'S WHEN I BEGAN TO WONDER IF I DIDN'T HAVE **MIXED** FEELINGS TOWARD YOU-

HOW COULD I EVER AGAIN KNOW THAT MY IMPULSE TO STROKE YOU WAS NOT **REALLY** A DISGUISE FOR MY IMPULSE TO SMACK YOU?

SO TO SAVE US BOTH FROM MY IMPULSES, I NO LONGER GO NEAR YOU.

THAT'S WHY I WATCH ALL THIS TELEVISION.

ME TOO, SAM.

NO MATTER THE EXOTIC PLACES I WENT, THE STIMU-LATING PEOPLE I MET-

I NEVER FELT QUITE ALIVE.

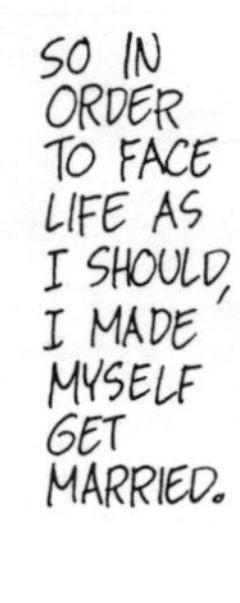
SO IN ORDER TO FACE LIFE AS I SHOULD, I MADE MYSELF GET MARRIED.

BUT DESPITE THE MYSTERY OF LOVE, THE GIVE AND TAKE OF HOME-MAKING-

I STILL DIDN'T FEEL QUITE ALIVE.

SO IN ORDER TO FEEL LIFE AS I SHOULD, I MADE US HAVE A BABY.

BUT REGARD-LESS OF ITS LOVING NA-TURE, ITS CONSTANT NEEDS -

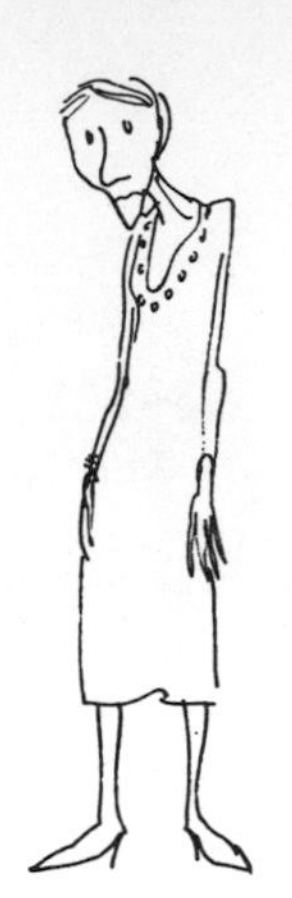
MY BABY FAILED TO MAKE ME FEEL QUITE ALIVE.

SO IN ORDER TO FACE LIFE AS I SHOULD, I WENT BACK INTO TEACHING.

BUT NOT-WITHSTANDING MY NEW PRESTIGE, MY POWER FOR GOOD -

I NEVER MANAGED TO FEEL QUITE ALIVE.

SO I GAVE UP MY STRUGGLE FOR LIFE AND STARTED GOING TO MOVIES ALL DAY.

GOD, I FEEL ALIVE!

I WAS DANCING MERRILY ALONG WHEN I SPOTTED A LOVE-LESS COUPLE SITTING ON A PARK BENCH.

"I WILL GIVE THIS LOVELESS COUPLE LOVE," I SAID TO MYSELF. AND SO SAYING, I SHOT AN ARROW INTO THE WOMAN'S HEART.

THE WOMAN SIGHED. "WHAT IS IT?" THE MAN ASKED. "WHY SHOULD YOU CARE?" THE WOMAN REPLIED. "DON'T START UP AGAIN," THE MAN SAID. "WELL, IF YOU MUST KNOW IT'S MY HEART," THE WOMAN SAID. "AGAIN?" THE MAN SAID. "YOU'RE SURE IT'S NOT YOUR NERVES TODAY?"

I SHOT AN ARROW INTO THE MAN'S HEART. "OUCH," THE MAN SAID. "STOP TRYING TO TAKE THE ATTENTION OFF OF ME," THE WOMAN SAID. "I GOT THIS TERRIBLE PAIN," THE MAN SAID AND GRABBED HIS CHEST. "WHAT DID I TELL YOU? TOO MANY CIGARETS!" THE WOMAN SAID.

I SHOT TWO MORE ARROWS INTO EACH OF THEM. "DON'T WORRY ABOUT ME," SAID THE WOMAN, FALLING OFF THE BENCH. "YOU AND YOUR HEAVY MEALS!" THE MAN SCREAMED DOUBLING OVER.

I SHOT MY LAST TWO ARROWS. "IF I WERE TO DIE, HARRY, WOULD YOU SAY SOMETHING NICE?" THE WOMAN ASKED. THE MAN LOOKED AT HER IN DISGUST, "ARE YOU STARTING UP AGAIN?" AND HE STAGGERED OFF.

THE WOMAN SAT ALONE GASPING FOR AWHILE. THEN SHE TOO STAGGERED OFF.

I STAGGERED OFF IN ANOTHER DIRECTION.

WHEN DORIS GAVE ME THE ULTIMATUM THAT WE EITHER GET ENGAGED OR WE BREAK UP I NEARLY WENT CRAZY.

I TOLD DORIS GETTING ENGAGED, FOR ME, WAS A **TRAP**. THAT I'D COME TO HATE HER IF SHE MADE ME GIVE UP MY FREEDOM.

AFTER WE'D BEEN ENGAGED THREE YEARS AND DORIS GAVE ME THE ULTIMATUM THAT WE EITHER GET MARRIED OR WE BREAK UP I NEARLY WENT OUT OF MY MIND.
I ASKED DORIS WHY NOW THAT I HAD BEGUN TO GROW AS A PERSON BECAUSE OF BEING ENGAGED DID SHE HAVE TO LIMIT MY FURTHER DEVELOPMENT BY MAKING ME **MARRY** HER?

ON OUR SECOND ANNIVERSARY WHEN DORIS GAVE ME THE ULTIMATUM ABOUT THE BABY I NEARLY WENT OUT THE WINDOW.

I TOLD DORIS BEING MARRIED WAS THE MOST INSPIRING EXPERIENCE IN MY LIFE-WHY SPOIL IT WITH A KID?

LITTLE LEROY IS FOUR NOW-THE MOST ADORABLE CHILD IN THE WORLD. YESTERDAY DORIS GAVE ME AN ULTIMATUM ABOUT HAVING A SECOND KID AND MOVING TO THE SUBURBS.
I'LL ARGUE. I'LL SCREAM. EVENTUALLY WE'LL DO IT.

FORTY YEARS OLD, DOING WELL IN THE MARKET, SUCCESSFUL IN MY CAREER, ACTIVE IN MY COMMUNITY, POLITICALLY AWARE-AND, AFTER ALL THIS, WHAT AM I?

DAGWOOD BUMSTEAD.

JERRY DOWN AT THE OFFICE, HE'S FOOLING AROUND BEHIND HIS WIFE'S BACK WITH RENEE THE BOOKKEEPER. YOU KNOW WHAT I TELL HIM?
JOHN, I'M GOING CRAZY.

I SAY TO HIM: "JERRY, I DON'T UNDERSTAND YOU GUYS WHO GO FOOLING AROUND WITH OTHER WOMEN. MY JOANNIE IS SIX DIFFERENT KINDS OF WOMEN AND THAT'S ENOUGH FOR ONE MAN.
PLEASE LISTEN, JOHN.

"SHE'S A WIFE, MOTHER, SISTER, DAUGHTER, SWEETHEART, BEST FRIEND. HOW MANY WOMEN CAN A GUY WANT?
JOHN, I'M GOING CRAZY.

"EVERY NIGHT," I TELL HIM, "IT'S A NEW EXPERIENCE. FOR FIFTEEN YEARS I COME HOME, JOANNIE'S WAITING THERE WITH A SURPRISE."
PLEASE LISTEN FOR ONCE, JOHN. I

SO HERE I AM HOME, BABY. WHO YOU GONNA BE FOR JOHN TONIGHT?
MYSELF.

WHY, WHEN I'M IN SUCH A GOOD MOOD, DO YOU HAVE TO START A FIGHT?

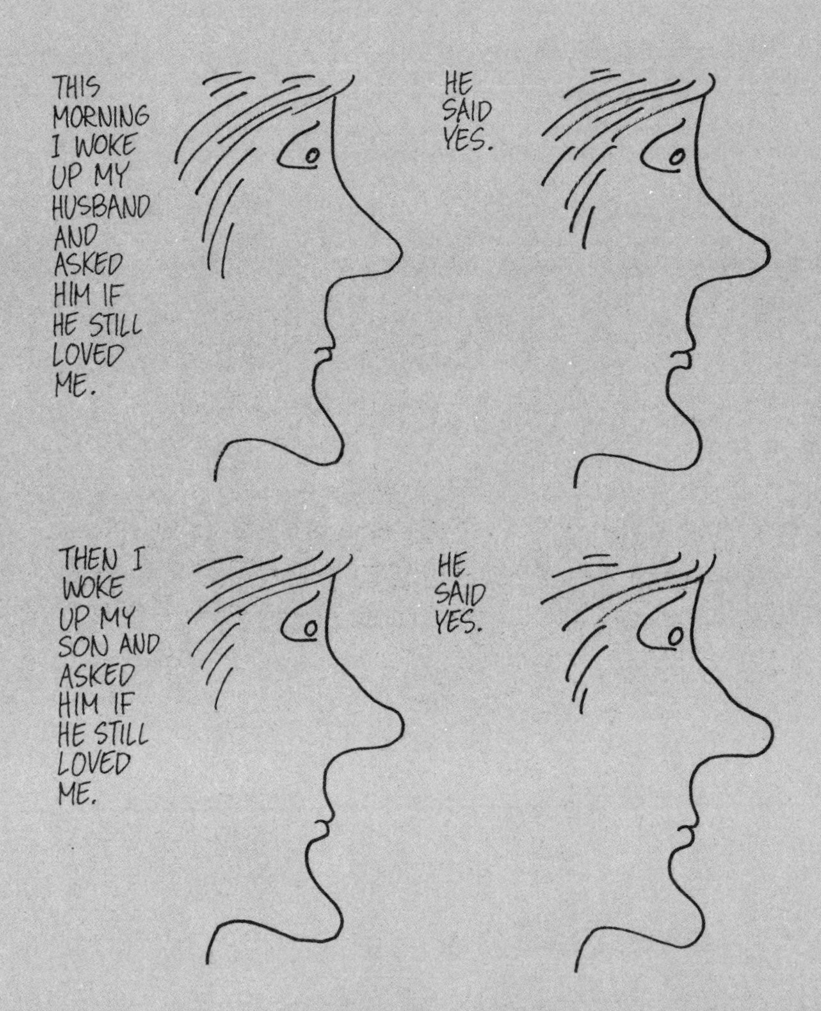
THIS MORNING I WOKE UP MY HUSBAND AND ASKED HIM IF HE STILL LOVED ME.
HE SAID YES.
THEN I WOKE UP MY SON AND ASKED HIM IF HE STILL LOVED ME.
HE SAID YES.

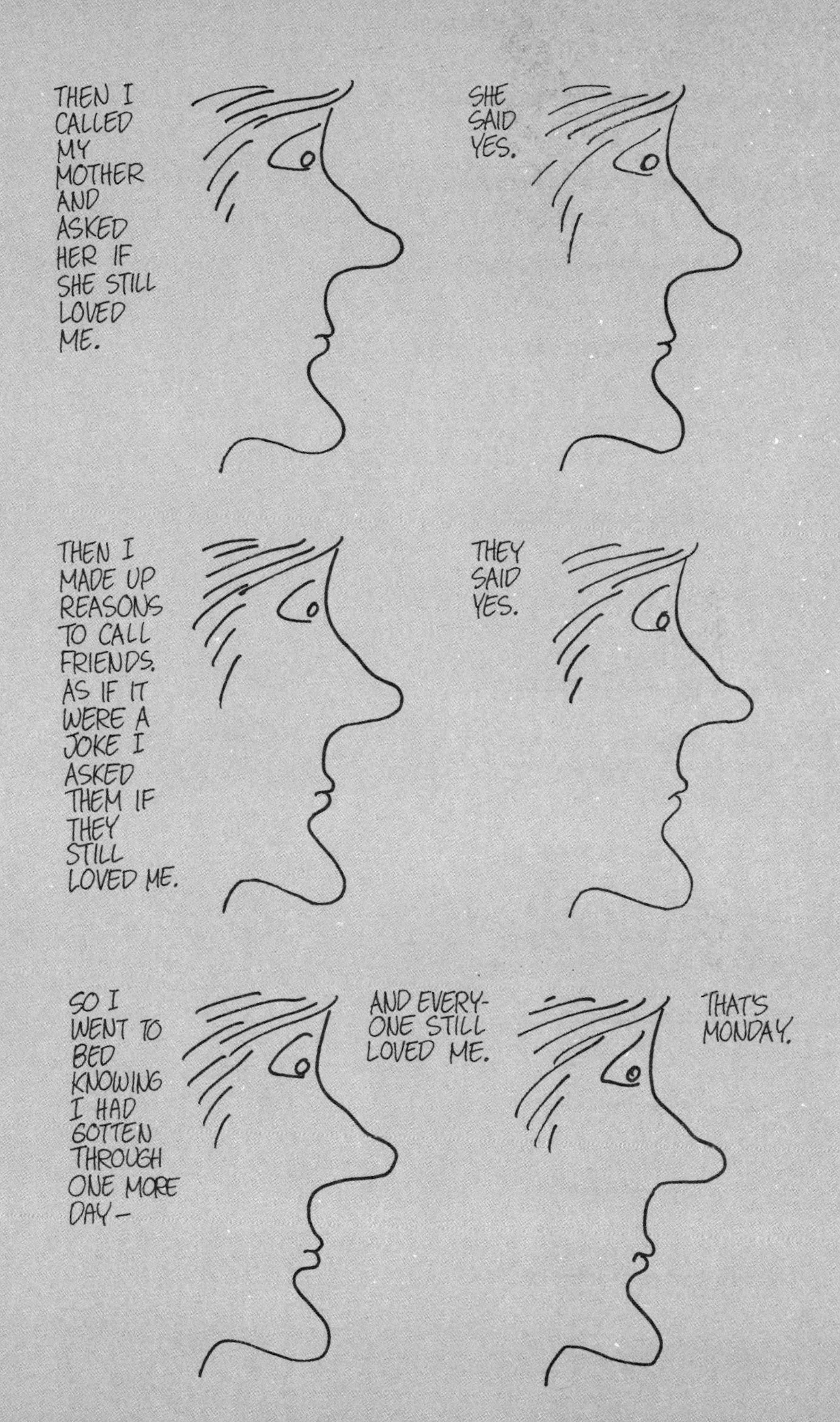
THEN I CALLED MY MOTHER AND ASKED HER IF SHE STILL LOVED ME.
SHE SAID YES.
THEN I MADE UP REASONS TO CALL FRIENDS. AS IF IT WERE A JOKE I ASKED THEM IF THEY STILL LOVED ME.
THEY SAID YES.
SO I WENT TO BED KNOWING I HAD GOTTEN THROUGH ONE MORE DAY—
AND EVERY-ONE STILL LOVED ME.
THAT'S MONDAY.

WHO KNOWS WHAT'S THE MATTER WITH HIM? I'LL TELL YOU WHAT'S THE MATTER WITH HIM. **I** HAVE FRIENDS AND **HE** DOESN'T!

HE SAYS EVERY NIGHT WHEN HE COMES HOME I'M ON THE PHONE TO EITHER **DORIS** OR **SHEILA**. WELL, **SURE** IT'S AN EXAG-GERATION. IT'S IN HIS **MIND** BECAUSE HE'S **JEALOUS**!

NO, HE REALLY **IS**, DORIS. HE SAYS I SPEND SO MUCH TIME TALKING TO MY **GIRL** FRIENDS I HAVE **NO** WORDS LEFT FOR MY **HUSBAND**!
THAT'S WHY HE SAYS I ALWAYS GO TO **BED** AT NINE O'CLOCK.

I **TELL** HIM I GO TO BED AT NINE O'CLOCK BECAUSE IT'S NO EASY JOB MANAGING A HOUSEHOLD. I HAVE TO GET OFF, DEAR. I HEAR HIM COMING.
I'M HOME, HONEY

I'LL CALL YOU AFTER I GET TO BED AT NINE. REMIND ME TO TELL YOU ABOUT MY FIGHT WITH THE LANDLORD AND MY SISTER'S KID AT THE DENTISTAND THE NEWCAR, IT'SALEMON-
HONEY, I'M HOME!

ANDTHEMARVELOUSCOTTON-SHEATHISAWDOWNTOWNAND-MYNEWHAIRCUTANDTHEMUG-GINGINTHENEXTBUILDING-
HONEY?

HI, ANGEL!
HI, HONEY!

UM-
UM-

IT STARTED WHEN I WAS A LITTLE KID AND I WAS PLAYING BALL AND I WAS IN A TIGHT SPOT- SO INSIDE MY HEAD I BEGAN **ANNOUNCING** MY WAY THROUGH THE BALL GAME:-"O.K. THE COUNT IS THREE AND TWO. JOEY STEPS OUT OF THE BOX. DIGS A TOE INTO THE DIRT. O.K.-HE'S BACK IN NOW. HE CHECKS THE RUNNERS. HE'S INTO THE WINDUP. AND HERE'S THE PITCH-"

FROM THAT POINT ON, INSIDE MY HEAD I ANNOUNCED MY WAY THROUGH **EVERYTHING**! SCHOOL FOR INSTANCE:- "THE OLD SECOND HAND IS TICKING AWAY. THREE MINUTES TO GO IN THIS HISTORY EXAM. JOEY CAN'T SEEM TO COME UP WITH AN ANSWER TO QUESTION 5. HE LOOKS OUT THE WINDOW. HE PICKS AT A NAIL. HE LOOKS OVER AT THE OTHER KIDS- AND, **WAIT** A MINUTE - **IS** HE? **YES**, HE **IS**! HE **PICKS UP HIS PEN**!"

AND EVEN **AFTER** I GOT OUT OF SCHOOL:-"THE SUPERVISOR IS LOOKING OVER JOEY'S SHOULDER. JOEY PRETENDS TO BE BUSY. THE SUPERVISOR HAS FOUND A MISTAKE. JOEY CAN'T SEEM TO LISTEN. THE SUPERVISOR ASKS JOEY IF HE UNDERSTANDS. JOEY SAYS HE DOES. JOEY STARES OUT THE WINDOW. THE SUPERVISOR MOVES ON-"

I EVEN ANNOUNCED MY WAY THROUGH MY MARRIAGE:- "JOEY HAS NOTHING TO SAY. JOEY'S WIFE HAS NOTHING TO SAY. JOEY'S FATHER-IN-LAW SAYS ISN'T IT TIME YOU WERE MAKING SERIOUS PLANS, JOEY? JOEY DIGS A TOE INTO THE CARPET AND STARES OUT THE WINDOW. JOEY'S LITTLE BOY SAYS, 'FIX IT, DADDY.'"

AND SO IT GOES. FROM EARLY MORNING TO LATE AT NIGHT. EVEN WHEN I'M IN BED:-"JOEY POUNDS HIS PILLOW. HE CLOSES ONE EYE. HE CLOSES THE OTHER. HE FEELS SLEEP COMING. IT'S COMING—. JOEY'S WIDE AWAKE. JOEY SNEAKS DOWNSTAIRS AND MAKES HIMSELF A DRINK—

"JOEY WANTS TO SCREAM."

EVERY MORNING I WAKE UP AND I SEE THE BLUE OF THE SKY.

AND THE AUTUMN BROWN OF THE LEAVES.

AND HEAR THE VOICES OF CHILDREN AT PLAY.

AND I BEGIN TO FLOAT.

LIFTED UPWARD BY A DEEP ABIDING HAPPINESS. FOR PEOPLE. FOR THE WORLD. FOR MY SMALL PLACE IN IT.

MY VERY SMALL PLACE.

WHERE I CAN NEVER GET ANY-THING DONE.

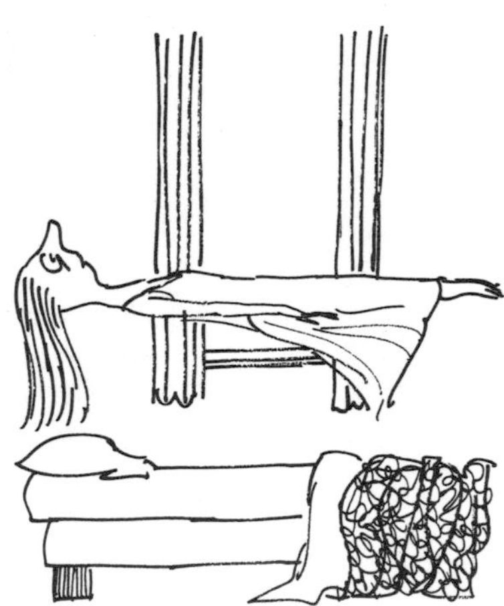

BUT JUST LIE IN BED ALL DAY AND WATCH THE SKY TURN GRAY, THE LEAVES DIE, AND LISTEN TO A BUNCH OF KIDS FIGHT.

WHY MUST ALL MY HAPPINESS BE JUST A COVER UP FOR DEPRESSION.

ONE NIGHT, DRIVING HOME TO EVENING COCKTAILS, I WAS SUDDENLY STRUCK THROUGH THE WINDSHIELD BY THE RAYS OF THE FULL MOON. —

AND I GREW BODY HAIR, POINTED EARS, CLOVEN HOOVES, AND A TAIL. —

AND I THOUGHT "AT **LAST!** IT'S THE **REAL** ME!" AND WITH FEAR SECRETLY MINGLED WITH DELIGHT I ARRIVED HOME— —

WHERE MY WIFE SAID, "YOUR DINNER'S COLD AND STOP LOOKING AT ME IN THAT ACCUSING WAY!" —

AND MY SON SAID, "ALL THE OTHER DADDIES ARE GOOD AT FIXING THINGS, YOU'VE GOT FINGERS LIKE **CLAWS**!"
AND MY LITTLE GIRL SAID, "WHY DO I HAVE TO HAVE THE ONLY FATHER ON THE BLOCK WHO'S **DIFFERENT**?"

SO I ATE THEM ALL UP.

WEREWOLVES REALLY SHOULDN'T MARRY.

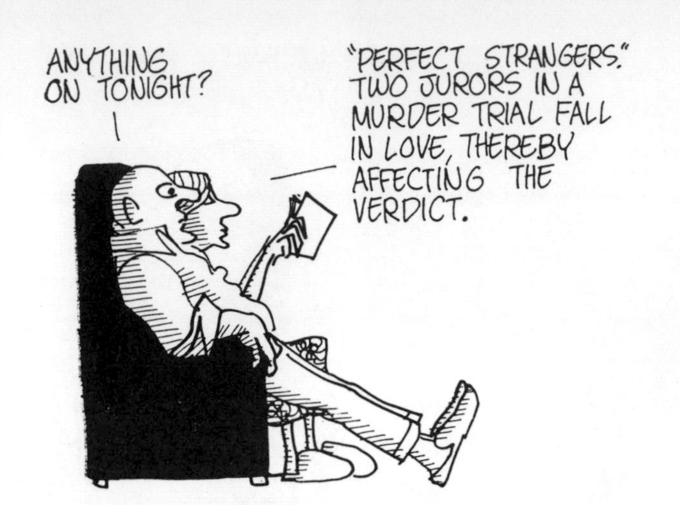
ANYTHING ON TONIGHT?
"PERFECT STRANGERS." TWO JURORS IN A MURDER TRIAL FALL IN LOVE, THEREBY AFFECTING THE VERDICT.

WE SAW IT. WHAT ELSE?
"THE BRIDE AND THE BEAST." BRIDE OF A HUNTER BECOMES ENSLAVED VICTIM OF A GIANT GORILLA.

WE SAW IT. WHAT ELSE?
"DEAD ON NINE." HUSBAND IS TRYING TO TEACH HIS BELOVED SECRETARY HOW TO SHOOT-SO SHE CAN KILL HIS WIFE, WHO WON'T GIVE HIM A DIVORCE.

WE SAW IT TWICE. ANYTHING ELSE?
"THE WORLD WAS HIS JURY." CAPTAIN JERRY BARRETT IS ON TRIAL FOR CRIMINAL NEGLI-GENCE AFTER LOSING HIS SHIP, PASSENGERS AND CREW.

WE SAW IT. ISN'T ANYTHING ELSE ON?
THE PRESIDENT'S SPEAKING AT NINE O'CLOCK ON THE WORLD CRISIS.

MAYBE WE COULD GO TO A MOVIE.

I LOVE YOU.
I LOVE YOU.
I LOVE YOU.
I LOVE YOU.

I LOVE YOU.
I LOVE YOU.
I LOVE YOU.
I LOVE YOU.

I LOVE YOU.
I LOVE YOU.
I LOVE YOU.
I LOVE YOU.
I LOVE YOU.
I LOVE YOU.
I LOVE YOU.
I LOVE YOU.

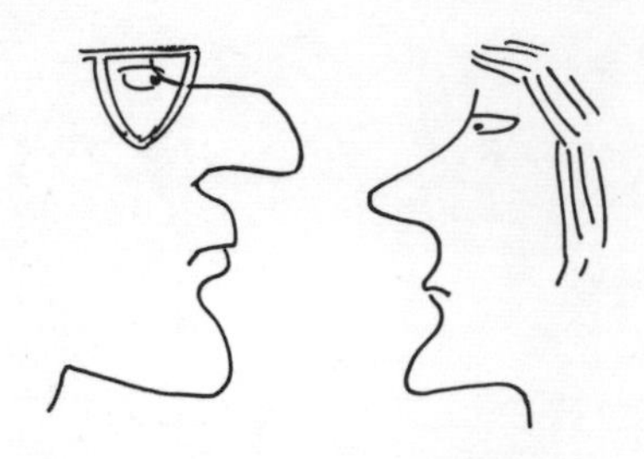
I DIDN'T SAY OUR
MARRIAGE WAS
A FAILURE.

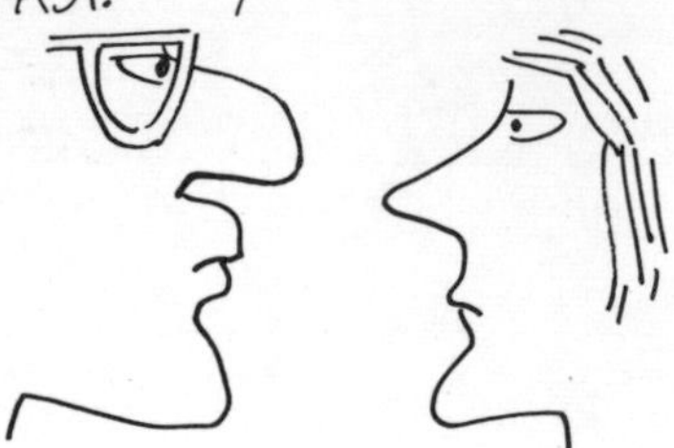
I JUST SAID THAT WE DON'T
HAVE EGGS IN THE HOUSE-
AND AFTER OUR LAST FIGHT
YOU PROMISED WE'D ALWAYS
HAVE EGGS FOR MY
BREAKFAST.

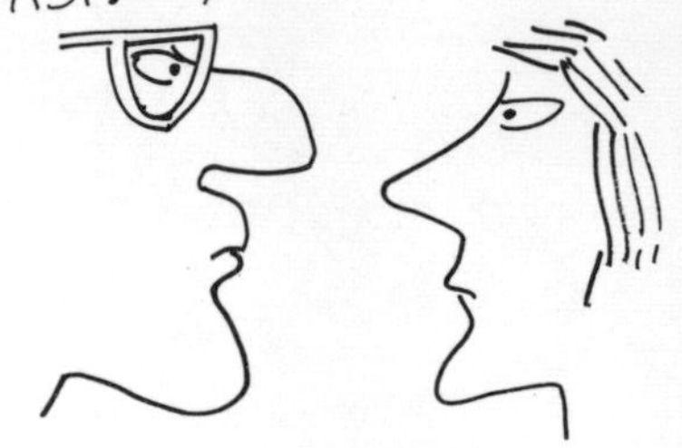
I JUST SAID WE DON'T HAVE
BUTTER IN THE HOUSE-
AND TWO FIGHTS AGO YOU
PROMISED WE'D ALWAYS
HAVE BUTTER FOR MY
BREAKFAST.

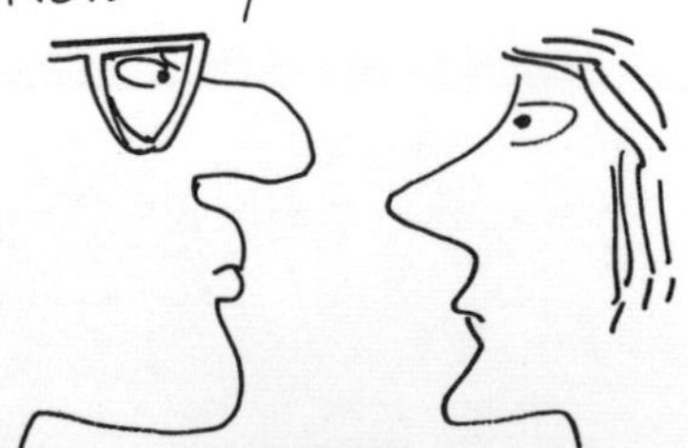
I JUST SAID WE DON'T HAVE
BREAD IN THE HOUSE-AND
THREE FIGHTS AGO YOU
PROMISED WE'D ALWAYS
HAVE BREAD FOR MY
BREAKFAST.

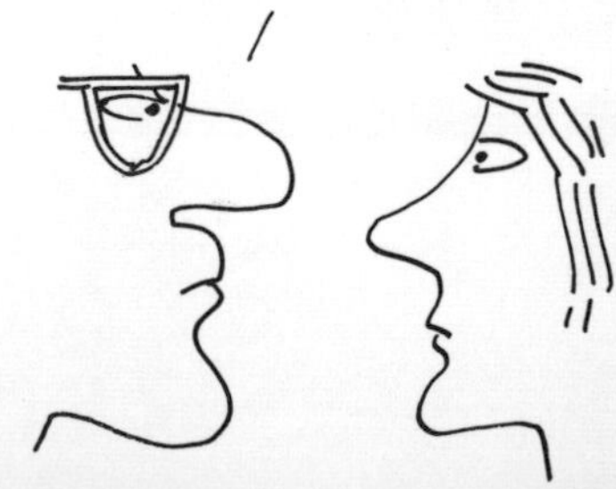
NOW, NOT HAVING EGGS,
BUTTER AND BREAD IN
THE HOUSE DOES NOT,
TO ME, IMPLY THE FAIL-
URE OF OUR MARRIAGE.

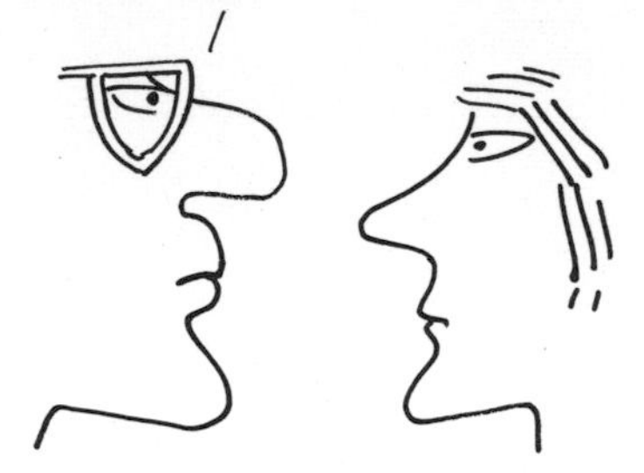
IT MERELY IMPLIES THAT WHILE I LOVE YOU, LOVE OUR HOME, AND LOVE OUR MARRIAGE -

CAN'T I HAVE ALL THAT AND EGGS, BUTTER AND BREAD IN THE HOUSE TOO?

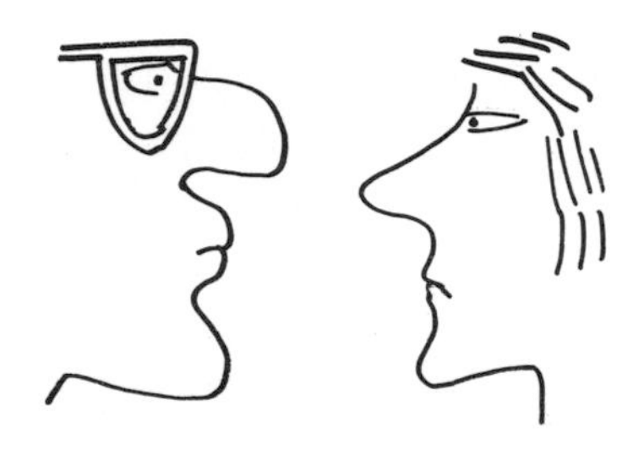

NO MORE DEALS, HARRY.

ONE NIGHT WE GOT HOME FROM WHAT I THOUGHT WAS A PERFECTLY LOVELY EVENING WITH MY NEIGHBORS AND I FOUND THAT CHARLIE WAS ABSOLUTELY FURIOUS WITH ME.
WELL, I FIND IT'S BEST WITH CHARLIE NEVER TO LET THINGS SIMMER. SO I SAID, "WHAT'S MY CRIME TONIGHT, CHARLIE? I THOUGHT WE HAD A PERFECTLY LOVELY EVENING."

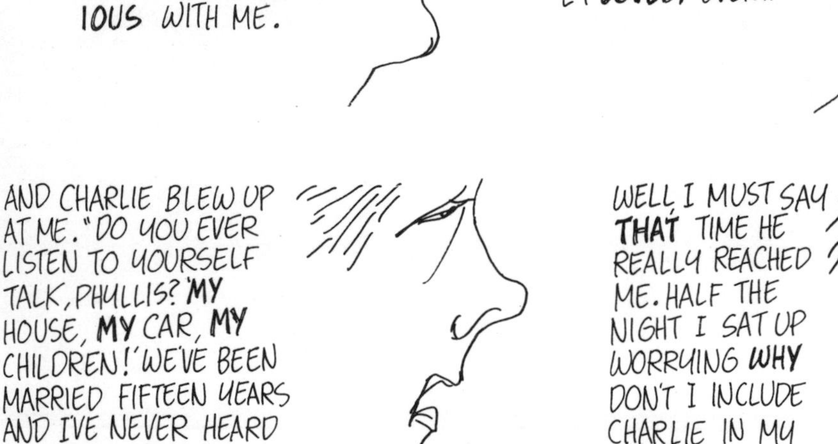
AND CHARLIE BLEW UP AT ME. "DO YOU EVER LISTEN TO YOURSELF TALK, PHYLLIS? 'MY HOUSE, MY CAR, MY CHILDREN!' WE'VE BEEN MARRIED FIFTEEN YEARS AND I'VE NEVER HEARD YOU SAY 'OUR'! ISN'T THERE ANY ROOM FOR AN 'OUR' IN THIS MARRIAGE?"
WELL, I MUST SAY THAT TIME HE REALLY REACHED ME. HALF THE NIGHT I SAT UP WORRYING WHY DON'T I INCLUDE CHARLIE IN MY LIFE?

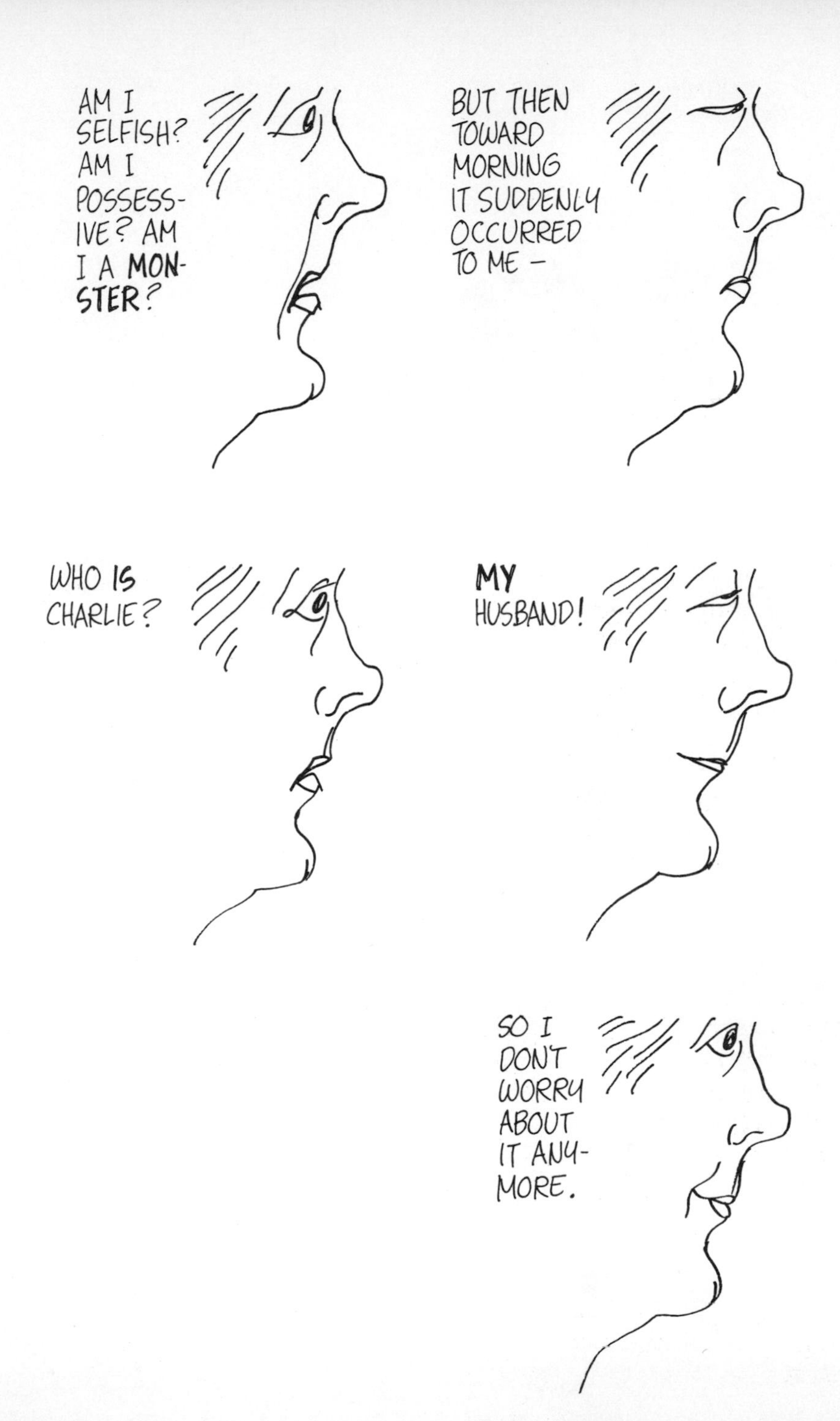
AM I SELFISH? AM I POSSESS-IVE? AM I A **MON-STER**?
BUT THEN TOWARD MORNING IT SUDDENLY OCCURRED TO ME –
WHO **IS** CHARLIE?
MY HUSBAND!
SO I DON'T WORRY ABOUT IT ANY-MORE.

WOW!
MMM.

WILL YOU LOOK AT THAT SUNSET!
MMM.

BEAUTY-FUL, HUH?
YOU CALL THAT BEAUTY-FUL?

CERTAINLY I CALL THAT BEAUTYFUL.
LISTEN, IF YOU CALL **THAT** BEAUTYFUL YOU SHOULD SEE MY WIFE'S ERMINE STOLE.

HOW CAN YOU COMPARE YOUR WIFE'S ERMINE STOLE TO THE BEAUTY OF A SUNSET?
MY FRIEND, TELL ME, WHAT **IS** BEAUTY?

THAT SUNSET! THAT'S BEAUTY!
NO! BEAUTY IS WHAT YOU AIN'T GOT MULTIPLIED BY WHAT YOU NEVER THOUGHT YOU'D HAVE.
S. S. Q.

I'M A PLAIN PERSON. I DON'T UNDER-STAND.
BEAUTY AIN'T A SOMETHING OUT THERE - LIKE A SUN-SET YOU'LL FORGET FIVE MINUTES FROM NOW. BEAUTY IS A SOMETHING THAT'S ALWAYS BEEN OUT OF YOUR REACH - UNTIL ONE DAY - YOU GOT IT! THAT'S BEAUTY!
S. S. Q.

SO YOUR WIFE'S ERMINE STOLE IS MORE BEAUTYFUL THAN A SUNSET.
MY WIFE, MY FRIEND, WORE RAGS FOR YEARS. RAGS! WHEN THAT DAY CAME WHEN I COULD AT LAST COME HOME WITH AN ERMINE STOLE - WELL, IN COMPAR-ISON - WHAT'S ONE LOUSY SUNSET?
S. S. Q.

THAT MUST BE SOME ERMINE STOLE.
A RAG. YOU SHOULD SEE HER SABLE.
S. S. G.

BEAUTY-FUL, HUH?
LIKE A SUN-SET.
S. S. G.

HAVE I GOTTEN TO LOOK FUNNY TO YOU, EDDIE?
YOU'LL ALWAYS BE MY BEAU-TIFUL BABY BABY.

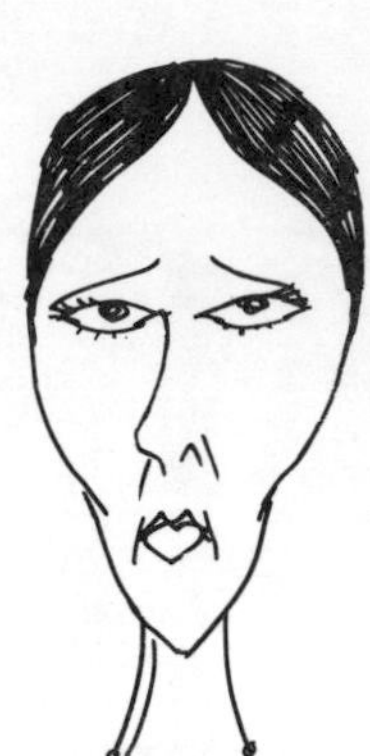
I MEAN IT, EDDIE. HASN'T MY SKIN BEGUN TO SAG A LITTLE?
YOU'RE AS BEAU-TIFUL AS THE DAY WE MET, BABY.

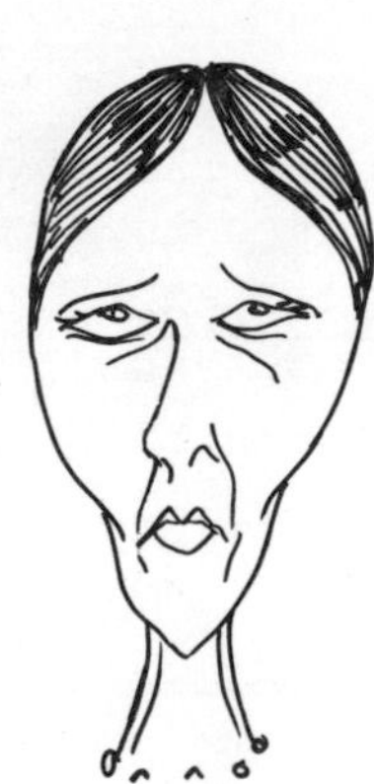
BE HONEST, EDDIE. HAVEN'T MY EYES BEGUN TO LOOK TIRED ALL THE TIME?
YOU'LL ALWAYS BE MY DREAM GIRL, BABY.

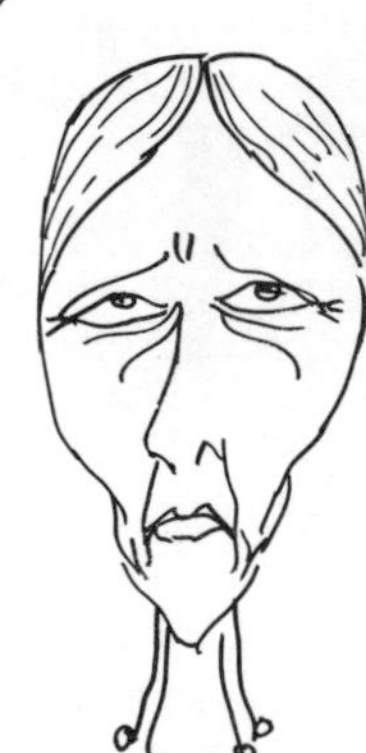
PLEASE TELL ME, EDDIE. HASN'T MY HAIR BEGUN TO TURN WHITE?
YOU HAVEN'T AGED A MINUTE IN THIRTY YEARS, BABY.

YOU ALWAYS LIE TO ME, EDDIE. AREN'T I GETTING VERY OLD?

EDDIE?

EDDIE?
EDDIE IS DEAD, MADAM.

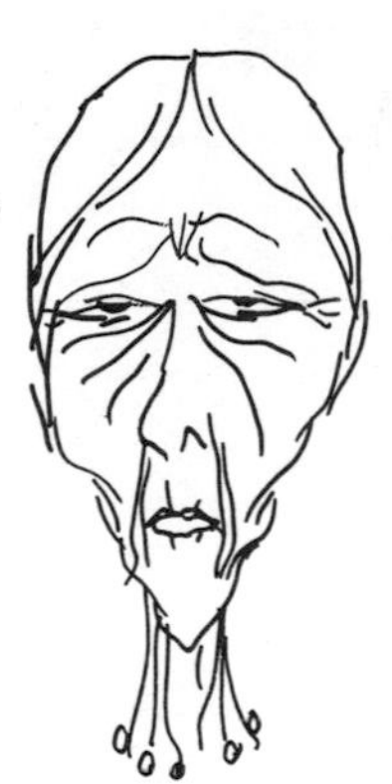
I NEVER COULD COUNT ON YOU, EDDIE.

MY WIFE ALWAYS USED TO SAY TO ME, "BILLY BATSON, YOU'RE SMALL, WEAK, INEPT, AND UTTERLY CONTEMPTIBLE! WHY COULDN'T I MARRY A **REAL** MAN?"

SO, ONE DAY, WHILE SHE WAS IN THE MIDDLE OF A TIRADE I LOST MY TEMPER AND DECIDED TO REVEAL MY **SECRET** IDENTITY!

SHE YAWNED FOR THREE WEEKS STRAIGHT. THEN ONE DAY I CAUGHT HER PACKING HER SUIT CASE –
SO I UN-**SHAZAM**ED MYSELF. –
POOF!

NOW MY WIFE SAYS TO ME, "BILLY BATSON, YOU'RE SMALL, WEAK, INEPT AND UTTERLY CONTEMPTIBLE! WHY COULDN'T I MARRY A **REAL** MAN?"

ONCE MORE WE'RE HAPPY!

MOTHER, AFTER THREE MONTHS' WAVING, YOU SAID YOU DIDN'T WANT TO GET IN THE WAY BUT AS LONG AS YOU WERE GOING BY OUR WINDOW EVERY DAY IRENE MIGHT, JUST ONCE, INVITE YOU TO DINNER.

MOTHER, I SPOKE TO IRENE YESTERDAY AND SHE WANTS TO COME BACK.

EVERY MORNING BEFORE LARRY COULD SEE ME DEAD AND BLOWSY I DRAGGED OUT OF BED AND TOOK 100 MG. OF SPEMOCLAGULATE—

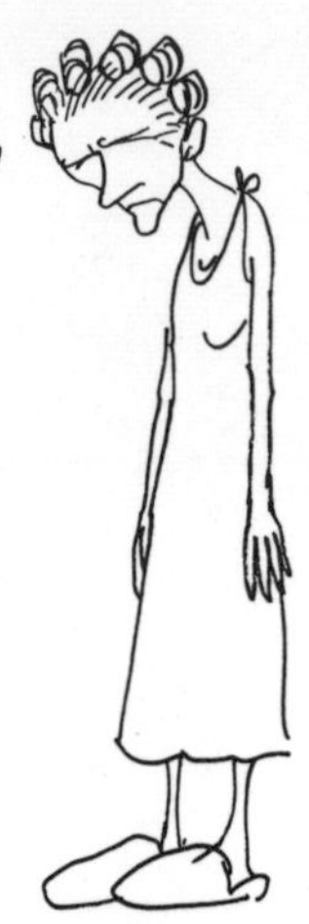

WHICH GAVE ME ENERGY THROUGH BREAKFAST—

WHEN I FELL INTO A SUICIDAL DEPRESSION, TAKING FOR IT 250 MG. OF PHENOAPTHAMINE—

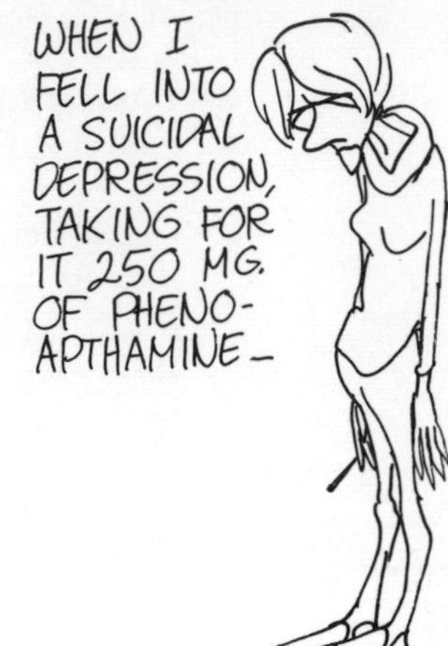

SO I'D BE CHEERFUL WHEN LARRY MADE HIS LATE AFTERNOON PHONE CALL—

AFTER WHICH I FELL INTO A SUICIDAL DEPRESSION UNTIL JUST BEFORE DINNER TIME—

WHEN I HAD TWO MARTINIS IN ORDER TO BE VIVACIOUS WHEN LARRY GOT HOME FROM WORK—

AFTER WHICH I HID IN THE KITCHEN WITH A SUICIDAL DEPRESSION UNTIL 10:30 -
WHEN I TOOK 500 MG. OF DIPHETOCAINE WHICH MADE ME ALERT AT BEDTIME WHEN LARRY DISCUSSED HIS DAY AT THE OFFICE -
AFTER WHICH I TOOK 750 MG. OF OSCU-LAVENOL AND SLEPT SOUNDLY THROUGH THE NIGHT.
THIS MORNING I WOKE UP DRAGGED MYSELF TO THE BATHROOM -
AND FOUND THAT I WAS ALL OUT OF EVERYTHING.
WHEN LARRY CAME DOWN FOR BREAKFAST HE SCREAMED: "WHO ARE YOU AND WHAT HAVE YOU DONE WITH DOROTHY?"

HEIGHT?
SIX FEET FOUR.
CLICK CLICK CLICK

COLORING?
DARK.
CLICK CLICK CLICK CLICK

PHYSIQUE?
MASSIVE.

TECHNIQUE?
BRUTAL.
CLICK CLICK CLICK CLICK CLICK

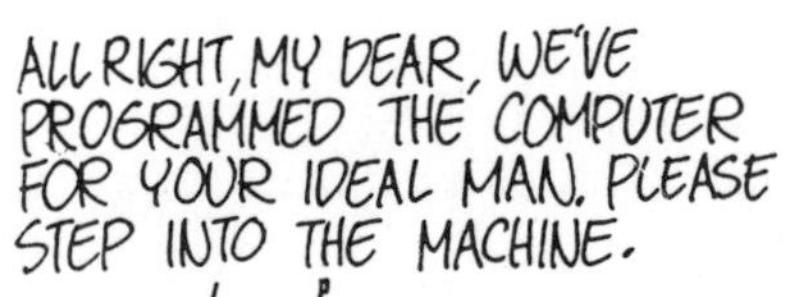
ALL RIGHT, MY DEAR, WE'VE PROGRAMMED THE COMPUTER FOR YOUR IDEAL MAN. PLEASE STEP INTO THE MACHINE.

CLICK
CLICK
CLICK
CLICK
NO!
NO!
NO!

CLICK CLICK
CLICK CLICK
CLICK CLICK
I HATE YOU!

CLICK CLICK CLICK
CLICK CLICK CLICK
CLICK CLICK CLICK
CLICK CLICK CLICK
I LOVE YOU!

EXTRAORDINARY!

AND IT DOESN'T **NECES-SARILY** DISPLACE MEN.
ON THE CON-TRARY. THINK HOW MANY WE CAN PUT TO WORK MAKING MACHINES.

LOOK OUT IN THE STREET, CHARLIE - SOME LADY'S BEING CHASED BY A GUY WITH A ROCK.
PROBABLY LOVERS. DON'T GET INVOLVED, DORIS.

HE CAUGHT HER. BOY, WILL YOU LISTEN TO HER SCREAM.
MIND YOUR OWN BUSINESS AND SHUT THE WINDOW, DORIS.

I WONDER IF WE SHOULD CALL THE POLICE.
DON'T BORROW TROUBLE. THE FIRST THING THEY WANT IS YOUR NAME.

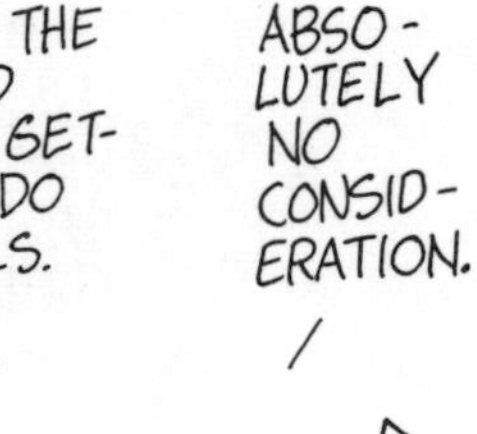

YEAH. THEN THEY PRINT IT IN THE PAPERS AND YOU START GETTING WEIRDO PHONE CALLS.
YEAH. ABSOLUTELY NO CONSIDERATION.

YEAH. ANY-HOW IT'S OVER. SHE'S JUST LYING THERE.
COME AWAY FROM THE WINDOW, DORIS. IT'S NOT OUR BUSINESS.

HEY, LOOK ACROSS THE STREET, CHARLIE - SOME GUY'S CLIMBING OUT ON THE WINDOW LEDGE.

WHERE?

THERE.

JUMP! JUMP!
JUMP! JUMP!
JUMP!

WHATEVER WE BECOME A PART OF WE LEARN TO LOVE.

WHATEVER WE LOVE WE MUST ULTIMATELY POSSESS.

WHATEVER WE POSSESS WE MUST FINALLY CONSUME.

WHATEVER WE CONSUME WE EVENTUALLY DESTROY.

LOVE YOUR ENEMIES.

IT'S TOO DANGEROUS AN EMOTION TO USE ON YOUR FRIENDS.